Barn Owl Trust

Barn Owls on Site
A Guide for Developers and Planners
by
Frances and David Ramsden

Illustrations by Glyn Jones

Cover Photographs:
Barn Conversions   David Ramsden
Barn Owl Portrait   Mike Read
Flying Owl (inside front)   Mike Read

©Copyright 1995 Barn Owl Trust
Published by the Barn Owl Trust 1995. ISBN 0 9525578 0 0

Registered Charity No: 299 835

The Barn Owl Trusts aims are to conserve the Barn Owl
and its Environment.
Funded by grants and donations, the main areas of the Trusts work
are conservation, education, information and research.
For more information about the Trust and its work please send a large SAE to:
The Barn Owl Trust, Waterleat, Ashburton, Devon, TQ13 7HU.

Acknowledgements.

This booklet is the culmination of five years research into the effects of barn conversions on Barn Owls, carried out by the Barn Owl Trust in the south west of England. We would like to thank everyone who helped to make this booklet possible including all of those who assisted with the Barn Conversion Research Project, especially Dr. Paul Chanin and Dr. Graham Martin.

Special thanks for help with this booklet must go to:

> Marie-Anne Martin and Keith Grant - for comments on earlier drafts.
> Glyn Jones - for illustrations.
> Mike Read and Paul Airs - for photographs.
> Sue Williams - for help with word processing.

Last but not least, we would like to thank the organisations and individuals who have assisted the Trust with funding during the past five years of either, the research and the report, this booklet, or both.

Many thanks to:
English Nature, Teignbridge District Council, The Panton Trust, British Telecom, J & L A Cadbury Charitable Trust, William A Cadbury Charitable Trust, Caradon District Council, D Curtis, Devon Bird Watching Holidays, Devon County Council, Duke of Cornwall, Dulverton Trust, East Devon District Council, Elmgrant Charitable Trust, Esmee Fairbain Charitable Trust, Sir Frederick Hiam Charitable Trust, Laings Charitable Trust, Manifold Trust, Mitchell Trust, Peter Nathan Charitable Trust, Norman Family Charitable Trust, North Cornwall District Council, P & F Charitable Trust, Restormel Borough Council, Skinners Co. - Lady Neville Charitable Trust, South Hams Environment Service, Torridge District Council, Totnes Round Table, R & A E Turner, Verdon Smith Family Trust, Vincent Wildlife Trust, A F Wallace Charitable Trust, H D H Wills Charitable Trust.

We hope that you will find this booklet informative and by using it will contribute to the conservation of this beautiful bird.

Frances and David Ramsden.
Waterleat 1995.

Foreword.

The archaeological record reveals that Barn Owls and Man have been neighbours since the Iron Age; this close relationship has survived right up to the present day. However, over the last fifty years, changing land-use and agricultural intensification have increased pressures on the Barn Owl. As a result, the Barn Owl population has shown a dramatic and alarming fall.

Barn Owls still make great use of old barns and other traditional agricultural buildings as breeding and roosting sites. However, it is these refuges which are now falling into disuse and disrepair or being converted to homes, driving out the Barn Owls. Research (in the south west) has shown that Barn Owl territories usually contain a number of roosting sites, but the loss of just one may result in Barn Owls abandoning the entire territory, rather than adopting a new site.

The aim of the Barn Owl Trust is not to prevent the conversion or development of old barns. Instead, it actively promotes ways to encourage the co-existence of Barn Owls and Man. This booklet, aimed at planners and developers, is intended to provide all the most useful information about Barn Owls and their housing needs.

On behalf of English Nature, I am delighted to welcome this positive approach by the Barn Owl Trust. I recommend the booklet to all those with an interest in these owls. If its guidance is followed, we can all look forward to the continuing co-existence between Barn Owl and Man.

The Earl of Cranbrook
Chairman of English Nature

20th March 1995

Contents.

An Introduction to the Booklet.

The Barn Owl (*Tyto alba*) was considered to be very common during the 19th century but has declined to such an extent that it is now a rare bird over much of Britain with some counties having only a few pairs left. As a result the Barn Owl is afforded special protection under the Wildlife and Countryside Act 1981 and has as much legal protection as any wild bird can have in Britain. Individual birds, their eggs and young are protected at all times and in addition nesting Barn Owls are protected against disturbance. As nests are usually located within buildings the implications for developers are wide ranging. For any activity involving disturbance to nesting Barn Owls a licence is required from the relevant Country Agency (English Nature, Countryside Council for Wales or Scottish Natural Heritage).

The increasing number of enquiries received by wildlife organisations and government agencies has highlighted the need for a publication to outline the implications of the legislation for development control and the effects of site loss on Barn Owls.
During the period April 1990 - January 1995 the Barn Owl Trust carried out a major research project looking at the effects of barn conversions on Barn Owls. The effect of the loss of occupied Barn Owl sites and the relative suitability of different types of alternative sites was investigated. This booklet has been produced to facilitate the recommendations contained within the Barn Conversion Research Project Report (see Appendix G).

Designed to present a positive approach to the development of occupied Barn Owl sites and to provide planners and developers with background information on Barn Owls and the problems the birds face, the booklet will enable the reader to carry out an initial site survey (to assess whether or not Barn Owls are actually using a site) and to take appropriate steps to minimise the effect of the redevelopment on any birds which may be resident. The emphasis is on working with and around Barn Owls rather than against them. The measures described are all relatively inexpensive and are most easily incorporated during conversion rather than added on afterwards.

Barn conversion is one way of ensuring that part of our architectural heritage is preserved. The Barn Owl Trust would like to see provision for Barn Owls incorporated into all rural barn conversions as a matter of course whether or not birds are present at the time of development. The simultaneous conservation of old barns and their resident Barn Owls may be achieved with the help of this booklet.

1.0: Background to Barn Owls.

1.1: Barn Owl Identification.

The Barn Owl is a very beautiful bird with pale golden buff coloured upper-parts laced with silver grey and white under-parts. It has a distinctive white heart shaped face and when seen in flight the overall impression is of a large white bird. Adult birds of both sexes are between 33-35cm from head to tail and have a wing span of approximately 85cm. Many people will recognise a Barn Owl from pictures, but in the wild the species is generally very elusive. The birds are most active just after dusk and just before dawn and as a result it is not unusual to find that people living close to an occupied site can be unaware of the birds' presence. Contrary to popular belief Barn Owls do not hoot. They do however have a considerable vocabulary of calls including screeches, hisses and snoring sounds.

1.2: Feeding and Habitat Requirements.

In Britain the Field Vole (*Microtus agrestis*) is the Barn Owl's main prey species; shrews and mice are also significant. During an average year a breeding pair of Barn Owls and their young may consume as many as 5,000 small mammals. In the breeding season most foraging occurs within about 1km of the nest. However, during the winter birds have been recorded at up to 4.5 km from their former nest sites. Food supply is the predominant factor governing Barn Owl survival and breeding success.

The ideal habitat for Barn Owls is rough grassland supporting a high density of small mammals. This can be in the form of linear features such as drainage ditches or woodland edge, or non-linear features such as young tree plantations or fallow pastures. Intensively grazed pasture, silage and arable fields yield little prey and the birds are not adapted to hunt within woodland. Nevertheless, Barn Owl Trust studies have shown that breeding Barn Owls are sometimes found with less than one acre of rough grassland within 1km of the nest. Thus even in areas of intensive grazing and cultivation the possible presence of resident Barn Owls cannot be discounted.

1.3: Breeding and Roosting Behaviour.

Barn Owls are often found in close proximity to man, making use of farm buildings, dovecotes, church towers, bale stacks and a wide variety of derelict and unused buildings, as well as hollow trees and cliff sites where available.
Site use falls into three main categories: roosting and breeding, roosting only, or visiting occasionally.

Occupied sites are usually free from direct or unusual disturbance, that is they are undisturbed or provide opportunities for the birds to remain unseen. Breeding sites must have a large cavity or wide ledge as Barn Owls do not build a nest but require a level surface on which to lay eggs. Modern farm buildings are not generally suitable as breeding sites unless nestboxes are provided.

A pair of Barn Owls may use several sites in their home range e.g.: a breeding site, several roosting sites and sites that they visit occasionally. However, some pairs seem to use their breeding site as their only roosting place all year round.

Once established, adult Barn Owls show an incredible amount of site fidelity i.e. they usually remain faithful to their sites from one year to the next. There is a growing body of evidence to suggest that the sedentary behaviour and site fidelity shown by established adult Barn Owls has survival value. Birds which know their home ranges intimately are more likely to survive and produce more young.

Barn Owls have been found breeding in all months of the year, but most eggs are laid in April and May. The eggs are white, (see picture 10) and are laid at about 2.5 day intervals. The female begins to incubate as soon as the first egg is laid. With a mean clutch size of 5.8, an incubation period of 31 days and an average fledging age of 62.5 days (9 weeks), it can be calculated that nests are occupied by eggs or young for an average duration of 108 days (3.5 months).   Fledged young often return to the nest but have normally moved on by their fourteenth week.
Second and very rarely, even third, broods may occur.

2.0: Problems Facing Barn Owls.

2.1: Barn Owl Decline.

There is no doubt that Britain's Barn Owl population has suffered a severe decline, although the evidence for this is largely anecdotal. Owing to its lifestyle, the Barn Owl is not an easy species to survey and as a result the national population can only be estimated. The comparison of various estimates would seem to indicate a decline of approximately 70% since the 1930s. Although it is still widely distributed over much of Britain, the species population density is considered to be critically low over much of its range and the Barn Owl is listed as a 'threatened' species in the Red Data Book.

2.2: The Loss of Prey-Rich Habitat.

Intensive farming methods have resulted in the loss of good foraging areas (particularly rough grassland) through increased arable farming and intensive grassland management. Although arable farming and areas of short-cropped grass may provide some food for Barn Owls, it is generally considered that such impoverished habitats are unlikely to support birds during the winter or enable breeding to take place. Winter survival in Barn Owls is closely linked to food availability and the first year survival rate is only 20-25%. Food availability also exerts a powerful influence over breeding success. On average breeding Barn Owls manage to fledge just 2.6 young per year.

2.3: The Loss of Roosting and Breeding Sites.

Old barns used by Barn Owls are disappearing from the countryside as a result of demolition and decay. The conversion of barns and redevelopment of derelict cottages has contributed to site loss as it is very unusual for any provision for Barn Owls to be incorporated. Hollow trees are also used by Barn Owls, but unfortunately these have also disappeared as a result of decay, Dutch elm disease, hedgerow loss and the general tidying-up of the countryside. Modern barns are more numerous than old barns, but are generally unsuitable for the birds as they lack dark cavities for roosting and breeding.

In areas with numerous potential Barn Owl sites, one would expect that the loss of an occupied site would have a minimal affect on the resident(s) who would simply move to another nearby site. However, research by the Barn Owl Trust has shown that in many cases the birds are reluctant to move in this way. Furthermore, other occupied sites may be abandoned when one site is lost and the birds may disappear entirely from the locality.

2.4: Other Problems.

Apart from the loss of habitat and sites there is a range of other problems which Barn Owls may face during their lives (which are frequently very short). Periods of prolonged rain or snow cover can reduce food availability. Road deaths account for 60% of known Barn Owl mortality. Drowning in water troughs is not uncommon. Barn Owls can be exposed to secondary poisoning by eating poisoned rodents. Barn Owl Trust leaflet No. 21 "Rat Poisons and Other Hazards" has more information on these topics.

3.0: Barn Owls and the Law.

3.1: Legal Protection and Law Enforcement.

With the introduction of the Wildlife and Countryside Act 1981 all previous laws relating to the protection of Barn Owls were repealed and re-enacted with amendments. Under Part 1 of the Act all wild birds (except pest species) are afforded protection. However, where an offence involves Barn Owls (or other "Schedule 1" species) the offender is liable to special penalties.

It is an offence to (and an offence to attempt to):-

a)   Kill, injure, or take (handle) any wild Barn Owl.
b)   Take, damage or destroy any wild Barn Owl nest whilst in use or being "built" (Barn Owls do not "build" a nest but may make a nest scrape).
c)   Take or destroy a wild Barn Owl egg.

d)   Have in one's possession a wild Barn Owl (dead or alive), or egg, (unless one can show that it was obtained legally).

e)   Disturb any wild Barn Owl whilst "building" a nest or whilst in, on, or near a nest containing eggs or young.

f)   Disturb any dependent young of wild Barn Owls.

It is NOT an offence to:-

g)   Take (handle) a disabled wild Barn Owl (unless you unlawfully disabled it) solely for the purpose of tending it until fully recovered and then returning it to the wild.

NOTE:
A person shall not be guilty of an offence by reason of any act made unlawful by these provisions if he or she shows that the act was the incidental result of a lawful operation and could not reasonably have been avoided.

Under Part 1 (section 25) local authorities are given the function of bringing this legislation to the attention of the public and may institute proceedings for any offence committed within their area. The police are empowered to enter onto any land and search, or stop and search any person, where an offence is suspected (section 14).

Any offence, or any attempt to commit an offence will render the offender liable to a fine not exceeding £2,000 per egg or bird involved.

3.2: Licences.

The Country Agencies, English Nature, the Countryside Council for Wales and Scottish Natural Heritage are empowered to grant licences for Barn Owl nest inspections. Licences are normally site specific and valid for a limited period of up to 9 months (January - September). Licences are not normally granted for the removal of Barn Owls, for the translocation of Barn Owls or active nests, or for killing Barn Owls.

3.3: Interpretation of the Law.

Just what constitutes "disturbance" is obviously open to interpretation. Generally what disturbs Barn Owls is the unexpected. Thus, normal frequent and regular human, animal or machinery activity within the same building as an occupied nest may not be disturbing to the birds. Conversely, any unexpected prolonged and/or noisy work within the building or close-by may be extremely disturbing to the birds and pose a major threat to breeding success.

Where disturbance to breeding Barn Owls or their dependent young is the incidental result of a lawful activity and could not reasonably be avoided, no offence has been committed. However, as soon as any evidence of Barn Owl occupation is apparent the disturbance may then constitute an offence. Whilst from the legal point of view the discrimination between incidental and wilful disturbance is important, from the birds' point of view the effect is the same. Increased awareness of Barn Owls amongst those involved in the re-development of old buildings should result in a reduction in cases of accidental disturbance and a reduction in instances where disturbance "could not reasonably have been avoided".

4.0 Barn Conversions and Barn Owls.

4.1: Regional Variation and the Loss of Sites.

Traditional agricultural buildings provide the majority of potential Barn Owl sites and are used by the birds to a greater extent than other types of site. There are however some regional variations within Britain. For example, in south west Scotland abandoned agricultural workers' cottages are important and in parts of eastern England the majority of known Barn Owl sites are hollow trees. In areas such as Devon the birds depend on the availability of old barns as there are very few derelict cottages or hollow trees and modern barns are generally unsuitable.

The supply of traditional buildings is finite and will eventually dwindle as conversion, demolition and decay continue to take their toll. Although barn conversion can ensure that some traditional buildings are preserved, (albeit in an altered state), where no provision for Barn Owls is made the effect for the birds is the same as demolition. Barn Owl Trust studies in

Devon have shown that in 1991, 10% of old barns had already been converted, 4% were undergoing conversion, and 20% were in a state of terminal decay or had already collapsed.

4.2: The Effects of the Loss of an Occupied Site on Resident Barn Owls.

The extent to which the loss of a single occupied Barn Owl site may affect the resident bird(s) is likely to depend to a large extent on the availability of alternative sites within the birds' home range. In areas with few old barns, derelict cottages, or large hollow trees it may be site availability which is the predominant factor limiting the Barn Owl population. In areas such as these (south west Scotland, for example) the loss of an occupied site may directly affect the overall population level. However, over most of Britain there are potential roosting and breeding sites which are unoccupied by Barn Owls and most old barns have long since lost their resident birds.

Where site availability is relatively high, one would expect to find that the loss of one occupied site had little effect on the birds'. However this is often not the case. In 1995 the Barn Owl Trust's "Barn Conversion Research Project" provided the first detailed information on this subject and found that the loss of one occupied site can have a remarkable "knock-on" effect. It is usual for resident Barn Owls to occupy more than one site; typically two or three roosting sites may be used within 1.5 km of the breeding site. The project showed that when one occupied site was lost, Barn Owls not only disappeared from that site but also abandoned other sites simultaneously and often entirely abandoned the area (within 1.5 km of the lost site), despite the fact that apparently suitable alternative sites were available within the area. The likelihood of this occurring may depend on the age or temperament of the individual birds concerned.

4.3: The Usefulness of Making Provision for Barn Owls.

There is nothing new about the idea of people sharing buildings with Barn Owls - there is evidence that Barn Owls were roosting in farm buildings as long ago as the Iron Age.
It is often thought that Barn Owls prefer isolated sites where there is little human activity, but this is simply not the case. Long before barn

14

conversions became fashionable there were cases of Barn Owls roosting and breeding in the attics of lived-in houses and cottages. Barn Owls residing in traditional farm buildings may tolerate the conversion of their home into a human dwelling and continue to occupy the site, provided that suitable provision is made. Regular human activity can be tolerated by wild Barn Owls, as long as the birds have a dark cavity, well above ground level, in which they can safely roost out of sight. Barn Owls can occupy modern structures, including rural industrial units, provided that these needs are met and food availability in the area is sufficient.

There is a lack of information as to exactly how Barn Owls select the sites they will (or sites they will not) roost or breed in within their home range. Occupied sites are presumably those deemed most suitable by the birds. Hence, where suitable provision for the birds is made allowing them to continue to occupy their chosen site, they may do so in spite of development pressures.

The cost of incorporating provision for Barn Owls during the development of a site is minimal. Barn Owls are such beautiful birds that, should the site ever be marketed, the presence of resident Barn Owls could afford the vendor a special selling feature with great public appeal.

4.4: The Importance of Timing.

Under the 1981 Act, active Barn Owl nests are afforded protection against disturbance, as are breeding adults and dependent young whilst at or near the nest. As nests are often situated in hidden cavities within old buildings or trees, it is not uncommon for the presence of an occupied nest to remain undetected until development of the site commences. Emergency situations where eggs or nestling Barn Owls are discovered when an old roof is being removed are all too common. Most of these "worst scenario" cases have arisen not because the nest was impossible to locate beforehand but simply because no preliminary search for signs of occupation was carried out.

As a general rule development during the breeding season should be avoided where there is any evidence of occupation by Barn Owls. In cases where a roosting only site is affected it is entirely possible that the development may have a detrimental "knock-on" effect if the Barn Owl concerned has a nest site nearby. Disturbance to such an adult bird may be deemed an offence and should be avoided.

15

The nesting period MUST be avoided at development sites where a building (or tree) which is a known breeding site is due for demolition or re-development.

Barn Owls have the longest breeding season of any owl species and active nests have been found in every month of the year, so a cautionary approach is called for. In buildings where fresh Barn Owl pellets are found it may be wise to assume that the birds ARE breeding and that no works should be undertaken until it is proved that they are not. Some roosting sites may be deemed to be roosting only sites because it is obvious that there is nowhere where the birds could possibly be nesting. If there are no other potential Barn Owl sites within 1.5 km it may be deemed that the resident bird is not breeding or that its nest is so far away that any disturbance would not constitute a contravention of the 1981 Act. Where potential breeding places are available within 1.5 km and evidence of recent roosting is found between March and August, it is best to assume that the bird is probably breeding nearby.

The nesting period is normally considered to be from the time that the female makes a "scrape" and lays the first egg until the time when the last "dependent" young stops returning to the nest site. This is the period during which disturbance must be avoided. As previously stated, eggs can be laid at any time of year. Normally however the first egg is laid in April, May, or the first half of June. The average date of first egg laid is May 9th. The length of the nesting period depends upon the number of eggs laid and the number of young reared. The absolute minimum time in which one newly laid egg could become a newly fledged Barn Owl is 87 days. With an average clutch and brood size the period from first egg laid to last young fledged is 108 days. HOWEVER, to these time periods must be added a further period of approximately 10 days, as newly fledged young habitually return to the nest whilst they are still dependent on the adults for food. At sites where one newly laid Barn Owl egg is discovered and the protection of breeding Barn Owls has called a temporary halt to the development, the delay will not normally exceed four months in total. It is unusual to find young nestling Barn Owls after the end of August unless the first clutch of eggs failed and a replacement clutch was laid or the birds are double brooding (breeding twice in one year).

In cases where development work awaits the completion of a breeding cycle a nest inspection should be carried out by a Barn Owl nest inspection licence holder before work is resumed (see Appendix F).

Picture 1. Nestling Barn Owls (eldest four weeks) showing fresh black nest debris on top of old cob wall in the month of June. *David Ramsden*.

Picture 2. The same nest nine months later (March) showing the previous year's nest debris which is now grey and dry. *David Ramsden*.

5.0: Initial Site Survey.

5.1: Search Procedure and the Identification of Signs.

When you first visit a potential development site in a rural area you may notice signs of occupation by Barn Owls. The first stage is to be aware that this is a possibility ! An Initial Site Survey can be carried out quickly and easily during a routine visit. Whilst inspecting the site look out for droppings, pellets, feathers and nest debris. Remember to consider your own safety when inspecting old buildings and trees.

Droppings - wherever birds perch they are likely to deposit their droppings. In dry locations Barn Owl droppings may remain for many months, even years. During dry summer months they may accumulate on roofs, fence posts or below tree branches. Most Barn Owl droppings are found on the floors of farm buildings directly below the roof beams where the birds perch. These appear as large white splashes on a hard surface or smaller white patches on old hay or straw (see picture 11). The droppings may run down the roof timbers and appear as white vertical lines (see picture 4). Where birds have perched on walls similar white lines may be noticed. The presence of droppings does not necessarily indicate occupation by Barn Owls as similar large white droppings are produced by various bird species. They are, however, a good initial indicator of possible occupation.

Pellets - Barn Owls generally swallow their prey whole and regurgitate the indigestible parts in the form of a pellet. Barn Owl pellets, composed mainly of hair and bone, often accumulate in places where the bird regularly roosts. Lots of different bird species produce pellets, including Tawny Owls, Little Owls, crows and even sparrows. However, Barn Owl pellets are quite easily distinguished and can be a reliable source of information on site occupancy (see picture 12). When fresh, Barn Owl pellets are moist, black and glossy and they vary from thumb nail size to whole thumb size (see picture 5). They are often rounded at both ends, but not always. If they have landed on a hard surface the pellets can be very flat on one side or one end. The drying and decomposition rate of pellets depends on where they accumulate i.e. pellets in a wet location can disappear quickly, whereas pellets in dry places may remain for several years and can be aged quite easily (see picture 6 and Appendix E).

18

Feathers - Barn Owls begin their first moult (with the exception of nestling "fluff") at about 11 months old, normally in the month of May whilst they may be breeding. The largest and most noticeable feathers (wing feathers) are normally shed during the months of May to October for females and July to November for males. Barn Owl feathers are very distinctive and can render reliable information on site occupancy (see picture 7).

Nest Debris - Barn Owls do not carry nesting materials and do not build a nest. If nests made of sticks are found within a building or tree hollow, jackdaws, stock doves or feral pigeons are almost certainly responsible. The minimum entrance hole size required for Barn Owls to gain access into a building or tree is about 7cm x 7cm (or about 8 cm. diameter if round). Buildings where Barn Owls roost or breed are usually over 3 metres high with the nest located in the uppermost part on a ledge or in a cavity. Barn Owls need a level area on which to lay their eggs, normally over 3 metres (and very rarely less than 2 metres) above ground level. Typical nest places within buildings are - top of wall (see pictures 1 and 2), between bales, wall cavity, nestbox, dry water tank, loft or attic floor, between stored items and wall, inside a chimney. Barn Owls will sometimes breed on top of old stick nests. Nests in tree hollows are normally located within the main trunk above ground level. In very large trees hollow side branches may be used. When searching tree cavities a torch and a small mirror is an advantage. Trees within an area of very dense woodland are not likely to be used by Barn Owls.

Note: If the initial site survey is during the main breeding season of March to August and there is any evidence of recent Barn Owl occupation of the site, DO NOT attempt to search any potential nest places. Consult your Local Office of the relevant Country Agency, English Nature, Countryside Council for Wales, Scottish Natural Heritage, (see Appendix F).

Outside the breeding season you may wish to check potential nest places yourself. Recently used nest places will usually have a distinctive smell (noticeable only at close quarters) and may show small pieces of white fluff which were shed by the nestlings. This fluff (mesoptile down) is distinguished from small feathers by the lack of an obvious quill; it is almost as light as air. Both the smell and the fluff are likely to have gone within a month of the nest being vacated. What remains is a layer of

Picture 3. *Right.*
An occupied Barn
Owl nestbox in the
roof beams of a
traditional farm
building.
David Ramsden.

Picture 4. *Below.*
When checking a
site for possible
occupation by Barn
Owls look out for
vertical white lines
down roof timbers
and walls.
David Ramsden.

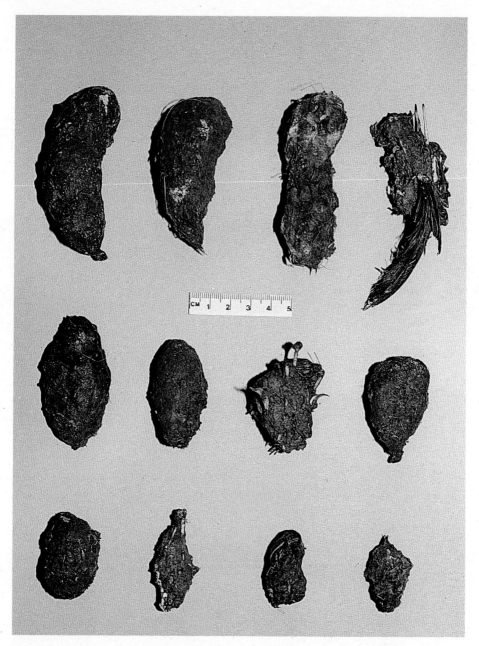

Picture 5. Barn Owl pellets showing a variation in size and shape.
David Ramsden.

pellet debris (see pictures 1 and 2). When searching a building for possible holes and potential nest cavities remember that some wall cavities are only accessible from the OUTSIDE of the building (see pictures 8 and 9).

5.2: Reading the Signs.

Assuming that evidence has not been removed by the action of humans, animals or the weather, in dry locations the signs may be read as follows (see pictures 1,2,4,6,7,11 and Appendix E):-

The presence of large white droppings means "Good, look harder"; the absence of large white droppings means nothing. The presence of only a few crumbling pellets means the site was probably used by a Barn Owl at least a year ago. The presence of approximately twenty pellets with a wide age range (from crumbling to glossy black) means the site has been visited occasionally for at least the past year. The presence of over 100 pellets with such an age range means the site has been used regularly over the past year, and so on.

The presence of only one feather may mean simply that one adult Barn Owl visited the site once during the summer. Remember that the presence of feathers is a strong indication of the site being occupied during the summer (May to November) by an adult (possibly breeding) bird.

If you are searching during the winter and find thirty pellets all about the same age - all dry and dark grey but still solid - and a few feathers, you can be reasonably sure that an adult Barn Owl roosted at the site for perhaps a month during the previous summer. If some of the large feathers are brown on one side of the quill with black bars (female) and other similar sized feathers are very pale or entirely white (male), then it is likely that an adult pair have both been roosting at the site. Therefore breeding within the site or somewhere nearby is likely. Feathers lying about become dirty and moth eaten in appearance and may become covered in cobwebs, allowing some indication of whether they were moulted during the current year or a previous year.

Anyone with a liking for a little detective work may become fascinated !

A Word of Warning

Although droppings, pellets and feathers can all render useful information, the absence of such signs DOES NOT necessarily mean that Barn Owls do not ever use the site.

5.3: How to Get Help and Who to Notify.

If, during an initial survey, some evidence of Barn Owl occupation is found, it is a good idea to inform the Local Office of your Country Agency - English Nature, the Countryside Council for Wales or Scottish Natural Heritage (EN, CCW, SNH). If it is thought that Barn Owls breed at or near the site of the proposed development the Local Office of EN, CCW or SNH should definitely be informed. If an active nest is discovered and the development has commenced or is imminent they MUST be informed immediately (see Appendix F).

If you require any further information on nestboxes, making provision for Barn Owls, habitat or any other Barn Owl conservation matter, you can contact the Barn Owl Trust who have a range of free Information Leaflets available by post or fax (see Appendix F). The Barn Owl Trust also offers a pellet and feather identification service for samples sent by post.

If a site visit is required by a Barn Owl specialist contact the Local Office of EN, CCW or SNH, and ask for the Species Protection Officer for your area, who can arrange for a holder of a Barn Owl nest inspection licence to contact you. Failing this, the head of the Licensing Section of your Country Agency (EN, CCW, SNH,) may be able to authorise someone to act on their behalf (by telephone) in cases of dire emergency.

For advice on bats or badgers again contact your Local Office of EN, CCW or SNH. For advice on other wildlife issues contact the Conservation Officer of your County Wildlife Trust (see Appendix F).
There are various organisations involved in Barn Owl conservation including the Barn Owl Trust, the Royal Society for the Protection of Birds, the Hawk and Owl Trust and various other voluntary groups. For help in your own area contact the Local Office of your Country Agency (EN, CCW, SNH) and ask them to recommend someone to you.

Where evidence of Barn Owls is found on site prior to a detailed planning application being determined the relevant local planning authority should be informed as soon as possible.

Picture 6. Barn Owl pellets showing a variation in appearance according to age (range - one day < thirty months). Note; these pellets were collected from dry locations, see Appendix E. *David Ramsden.*

Picture 7. Barn Owl feathers showing variation in size and colour. The presence of freshly moulted feathers is a good indication of site occupation during the summer (May - November). *Paul Airs.*

6.0: Planning for Barn Owls

6.1: Planning Applications - Outline Stage.

When an application for planning permission is made, even at this early stage, it is wise to inform the local authority ecologist that Barn Owls are present on site or that some evidence of occupation has been found. The application should be accompanied by a full supporting statement indicating which part of the site is known to be used by Barn Owl(s) and outlining your plans to accommodate the birds and minimise disturbance to them. This will indicate the co-operation of the developer in protecting the birds and help to avoid delays at a later stage. Nothing is worse for both sides than a situation where plans are approved, works scheduled and then the presence of Barn Owls is notified by a third party. Better by far to acknowledge the birds' presence from the outset and to work with them rather than against them.

6.2: Planning Applications - Full Application and Reserved Matters Stage.

Once outline permission has been obtained the practicalities of designing a scheme to accommodate both people and Barn Owls can be addressed. There is no reason why, with adequate foresight, they cannot exist alongside each other, even under one roof. Having determined which parts of the proposed development site are used by Barn Owls, you should attempt to incorporate the following measures.

a) Provide nestboxes in other nearby buildings (which are not due for development) following the advice in Appendix A.

b) Time the building works so as to avoid the birds' breeding season (March to August).

c) Shortly before building works commence, undertake a final search of each structure (or hollow tree) involved to ensure that no breeding is taking place.

d) Position noisy static machinery away from any buildings or trees occupied by owls.

e)   Prevent site workers from gaining entry into occupied or potential Barn Owl sites (on or near the site) which are not due for development so as to provide "sanctuary" areas for the birds.

f)   Incorporate provision for Barn Owls into the part(s) of the development site used by the birds following the advice provided by this booklet.

g)   Do not leave any steep-sided containers of water uncovered on the site (to avoid the risk of Barn Owls drowning).

h)   Position new tree plantings and overhead wires to allow a clear flight path for Barn Owls to and from the access hole(s) provided for them.

i)   Landscape the site to provide areas of rough grassland as foraging areas for Barn Owls and to encourage other native flora and fauna.

7.0: Protection Prior To and During Construction

At the earliest possible stage (prior to any building work commencing) alternative roosting and breeding places should be provided in the form of nestboxes (see Appendix A). These are best placed in structures where there is already some evidence of Barn Owl occupation as it is normally far easier to retain birds at existing sites than to encourage them into new ones.

Where evidence of Barn Owls is found in one of a group of suitable buildings it is probable that evidence will also be found in one or more of the others. If possible one or more nestboxes should be provided in these structures which are then designated "no-go" areas. Where the occupied site is a single isolated building (or hollow tree due for felling) and there are no potential alternative sites nearby, outdoor nestboxes should be provided in trees, on the outside of buildings or even on poles (see Barn Owl Trust leaflet No. 4. "Outdoor Nestbox Design"). Generally however, indoor boxes are easier to provide and may be preferred by the birds (see Appendix A).

Once boxes have been provided it is not a good idea to inspect them. Birds which have only recently occupied a site may be particularly

27

Picture 8. When checking a site for potential nest cavities don't overlook the outside of the building. Note the white lines on the wall to the right of the ladder.
David Ramsden.

Picture 9. This cavity (note the debris and droppings) was accessible only from the outside of the site and could easily have been missed during a survey.
David Ramsden.

Picture 10. Five newly laid (clean) Barn Owls eggs showing size variation and one hatched egg showing natural discoloration which can occur during incubation. *Paul Airs.*

Picture 11. Typical accumulation of droppings, pellets and feathers on old hay beneath a well used roosting place. Note the variation in coloration of the three wing feathers indicating probable occupation by a pair of Barn Owls. The presence of numerous feathers indicates occupation during the summer and the pellets are fresh (black).
David Ramsden.

29

sensitive to disturbance. As a matter of course all unnecessary disturbance should be avoided.

Never attempt to physically move a Barn Owl or its nest contents (see section 3.1: Barn Owls and the Law).

The aim during this pre-development stage is simply to enhance the suitability of alternative sites the birds are already using and to ensure that alternative sites are available in every case. This will help to maximise the chances of the resident birds remaining within their home range whilst the development takes place.

Established adult Barn Owls are naturally inclined to remain at the same site throughout their lives and may readily adopt any nestboxes provided. However where occupied sites are lost and no provision for the birds is made, the effect can be devastating. The birds may not only leave the lost site but may simultaneously abandon other sites they have been using within their home range.

Incorporating provision for Barn Owls in the redevelopment of an existing building should be done at the earliest stage possible. For example, when an old barn is being converted into a dwelling the roof is normally replaced. This is an ideal time to create a new entrance hole (if necessary) for the birds through the end wall close to the apex. As soon as the new roof is complete provision for the birds can be made by boarding off what will become part of the attic area (see Appendices B, C and D). Thus the building is ready for the birds to occupy before most of the conversion work has taken place.

Experience has shown that in such cases the birds may occupy the new provision whilst the conversion is completed. However noisy construction work close to an active nest must be avoided. Therefore the stage at which provision for the birds is made may be determined by the timing of the development in relation to the forthcoming breeding season (March to August).

7.1: What To Do if Eggs or Young are Discovered During Construction.

With the use of this booklet the chance of discovering an occupied nest at this late stage should be minimal. However, as Barn Owls sometimes nest in cavities which are inaccessible to humans it is possible for active nests to remain undetected until development of the site commences.

Such discoveries may be made when old hay or straw bales are moved, when roof sections are removed or hollow trees felled. Upon discovery of a nest the following steps should be taken:-

a) Stop work.

b) If possible quietly replace the object which had previously covered the nest (the last roof section removed, for example).

c) Inform the site foreman and warn workers to avoid additional disturbance.

d) Telephone the Local Office of the relevant Country Agency (EN, CCW, SNH) immediately (see Useful Contact numbers in Appendix F) and follow their instructions.

Normally the Country Agency will arrange for someone with a Barn Owl nest inspection licence to visit the site and will ask for work to be temporarily suspended at least until this visit has taken place.
Every effort is made to ensure that the development can continue in a way which is consistent with the birds' welfare and the law. The advice given will depend upon numerous factors, such as the age of the nestlings etc. It is possible that certain works may have to wait until the last dependent young has stopped returning to the nest.

If an incubating female Barn Owl has been flushed from the nest and eggs are discovered, the nest should be left alone as it is likely that the bird will return. Cases have been recorded where eggs have been temporarily abandoned for up to 24 hours and have subsequently hatched successfully.

8.0: Protection after Construction.

Landscaping the site may provide an opportunity for creating areas of rough grassland to encourage voles and shrews (the Barn Owl's main prey species). As Barn Owls normally forage over an area of at least

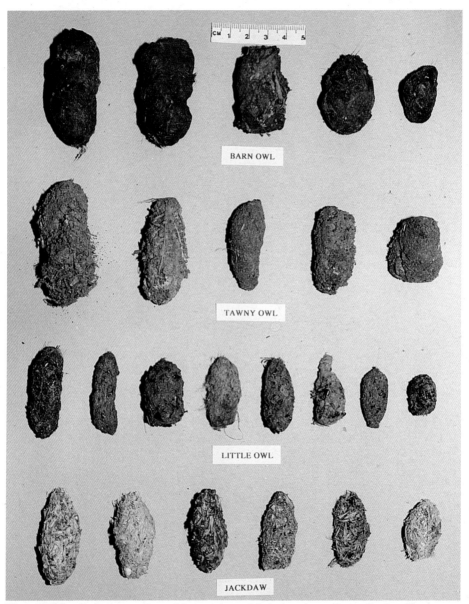

Picture 12. Pellets produced by various bird species. Barn Owl pellets are much darker than Tawny Owl pellets which are normally grey and may show insect remains. Little Owl pellets often show insect remains (Kestrel pellets are very similar). Jackdaw pellets are highly variable in content. *David Ramsden.*

3 sq km, most development sites are not likely to include much of the birds feeding area. However, within the intensively farmed landscape which covers most of Britain, it is small patches of rough grass which can tip the balance in favour of the owls. The birds may concentrate their hunting on quite small patches of long grass and commute from one to the next ignoring short grass or cultivated land. Thus the provision of even small areas of rough grass can be beneficial to Barn Owls as well as wild flowers, butterflies and other wildlife (see Barn Owl Trust leaflets No. 1 "Habitat For Barn Owls" and No. 2. "Rough Grassland Management"). The creation of new woodlands can be beneficial in the short term, as small mammal populations build up in the rough grass between the new plantings. However, the Barn Owl is not a woodland bird, therefore some benefit is lost as the trees grow. When planning a new copse allocate slightly more ground than is required to ensure a strip of rough grass remains around the trees. This should be cut occasionally to prevent scrub encroachment.

Nestboxes for Barn Owls do not need much maintenance provided that they are correctly designed, positioned and secured. Once erected, boxes should be left undisturbed, although a situation may arise where an inspection is desirable. The main reason for nestbox inspection is for monitoring purposes by ornithologists during the nesting period. This can only be carried out by someone with the appropriate licence and the site owner's permission. Another reason to inspect boxes is to check for occupation by other species. It is not unusual for instance for Jackdaws to fill large cavities with sticks to the extent that the cavity becomes too small for Barn Owls to use. The clearing out of boxes and maintenance inspections are best carried out between October and January when breeding birds are least likely to be encountered and a licence is not normally required.

If rats or mice are found to be a problem on site it may be necessary for rodenticide bait to be used. In order to minimise the risk to Barn Owls and other predators (from eating poisoned rodents) a preparation containing only WARFARIN should be used. Avoid using rodenticides containing Brodifacoum, Bromadiolone, Difenacoum, Flucomafen or Alphachloralose. Follow the manufacturers instructions carefully.

It is not uncommon for Barn Owls to be found dead from drowning in cattle water troughs or water butts. Most cases involve breeding females during the summer months. All steep-sided containers of water should be covered or should have a means of escape incorporated (see Barn Owl Trust leaflet No. 21 "Rat Poisons and Other Hazards" for further information).

8.1: Selling the Site.

Second only perhaps to the Robin, the Barn Owl is one of the best known of British birds and certainly one of the most attractive. Its decline and the conservation work undertaken on its behalf has received much publicity. As a result the Barn Owl is admired by many people from different walks of life. The presence of these magnificent birds would certainly be seen as a unique selling point by a significant proportion of home buyers who would welcome the opportunity to live alongside these beautiful owls. Barn Owls are easy to live with.

It is often surprising how much human activity wild Barn Owls can become accustomed to, provided they can tuck themselves away in a dark cavity high above the ground. Regular domestic activity is not likely to disturb the birds at all and experience has shown that Barn Owls can roost all year round and breed annually in the roofs of occupied dwellings with children playing, dogs barking, cars coming and going and bright outside lights.

There are of course a minority of people who don't like the idea of having birds in their attic, but once suitable advice has been given, genuine problems are virtually unheard of.

The Barn Owl Trust has produced a leaflet specifically for the owners of occupied Barn Owl sites. Where occupied sites are sold it is suggested that such information is provided to the new owners as a matter of course (see leaflet No. 28 "Guidelines for Guardians of Wild Barn Owl Sites").

9.0: Further Reading.

Barn Conversion Research Project Report, *Ramsden D.J.* (1995) Barn Owl Trust. Available by post (cost £10 plus £2 p&p) from the Barn Owl Trust, Waterleat, Ashburton, Devon, TQ13 7HU.

Barn Owl Trust Information Leaflets

No. 1   **Habitat for Barn Owls.**
No. 2   **Rough Grassland Management.**
No. 3   **Indoor Nestbox Design.**
No. 4   **Outdoor Nestbox design.**
No. 21 **Rat Poisons and Other Hazards.**
No. 22 **Barn Conversions - Provisions for Owls.**
No. 26 **Search Procedure for Buildings.**
No. 28 **Guidelines for Guardians of Wild Barn Owl Sites.**

Available free of charge. Please send a large SAE to the Barn Owl Trust, Waterleat, Ashburton, Devon, TQ13 7HU.

The Barn Owl. *Taylor, I. R.* (1989) Shire Publications, ISBN 0-7478-0024-3.

Barn Owls - An Action Plan and Practical Guide for Their Conservation in Scotland. *Taylor I.R.* (1993) University of Edinburgh. Available by post (cost £5.00 inc. p&p) from the Scottish Wildlife Trust, Cramond House, Kirk Cramond, Cramond Glebe Road, Edinburgh, EH4 6NS.

Badgers on Site - A Guide for Developers and Planners. *Cox, P. R.* (1993) ISBN 1851631682. Available by post (cost £3.00 inc. p&p) from Babtie Public Services Division, Shire Hall, Shinfield Park, Reading, RG2 9XG.

Bats in Roofs - A Guide for Surveyors. Available free of charge from English Nature, Northminster House, Peterborough, PE1 1UA.

Bats in Houses. *Hutson A.M.* Available by post (cost £1.20 inc. p&p) from the Bat Conservation Trust, London Ecology Centre, 45 Shelton Street, London, WC2H 9HJ.

Bat Information Pack - for Architects and Surveyors. Free of charge from the Bat Conservation Trust (address as above).

Appendix A.
Indoor nestbox, specification and positioning details.

Construction.

Indoor nestboxes for dry locations are often made using a packing case such as a tea-chest. Alternatively a purpose- built box may be constructed using 6 or 9 mm plywood and batten as necessary. Boxes made of thin plywood are lightweight and therefore easier to erect (see Figure 1 on page 37).
Don't use rain forest products, select Canadian or Scandinavian softwood ply. If a tea-chest is used, ensure that the foil lining and any sharp nails or strips of metal that might injure the owls are removed.

Please Note:
This design of box is only suitable for use within buildings. For details of an outdoor nestbox design please send for a copy of Barn Owl Trust leaflet No. 4 "Outdoor Nestbox Design".

Positioning.

Wherever possible, indoor nestboxes should be positioned as follows:

a)   Close to the place where the owls have nested previously.
b)   Within a building where there is some evidence of a Barn Owl roosting or visiting.
c)   Within a building with an owl access hole at least 3 metres above ground level.
d)   Within a building which is not subject to increased disturbance in the late winter or spring. Avoid farm buildings used mainly for lambing.
e)   At least 3 metres above ground level - normally at or near the apex.
f)   In order that the box entrance faces the owls entrance into the building.
g)   In the darkest part of the building.
h)   To enable the owls to have an easy flight path to and from the box.

Lining the box - although it is not necessary to put anything in the box you may wish to provide a layer of wood flakes or dry straw. Do not use sawdust, peat or damp hay.

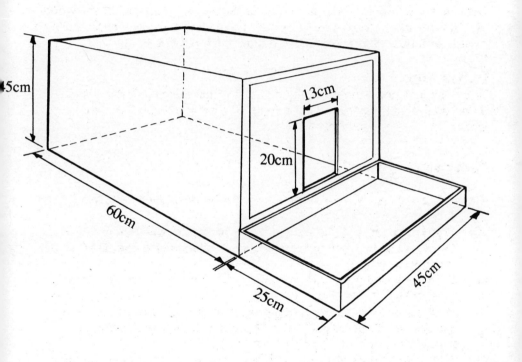

Figure 1. Indoor Nestbox Design.

Appendices B and C.

Provision for Barn Owls within Loft Areas.
See illustrations on pages 39 and 40.

There are numerous ways in which provision for Barn Owls can be incorporated into buildings. Where indoor boxes are provided in traditional agricultural buildings they are normally attached to the roof timbers as shown in Figure 3. (illustration overleaf). As Barn Owls seem to prefer an enclosed nesting cavity high above the ground the provision of a nestbox (see Appendix A) can greatly enhance the suitability of the site. In houses or barn conversions with a large loft provision for the birds can be made in this way.

In buildings with only a small loft the space may be so small as to make the provision of a nestbox impractical, the birds will then nest on the floor as shown in Figure 2. (illustration overleaf). As the young owls develop they will move around a great deal before they can fly, for this reason it is important to position the entrance/exit hole at least 40 cm above the level of the nest area to prevent the nestlings falling out. An adult Barn Owl needs a minimum of 40 cm headroom and the absolute minimum floor area recommended is 40 x 40 cm.

When deciding in which part of the development to make provision there are various factors to be considered. Wherever possible the entrance hole should be positioned:

a)   So as to allow the birds to enter the building in the same way as they did prior to the development.

b)   At least 3 metres above ground level.

c)   Avoiding obstructions such as trees and overhead wires.

d)   Facing away from the prevailing wind.

e)   On the side of the site which will be the least disturbed, after the completion of the development.

f)   Overlooking open countryside and visible to any passing birds.

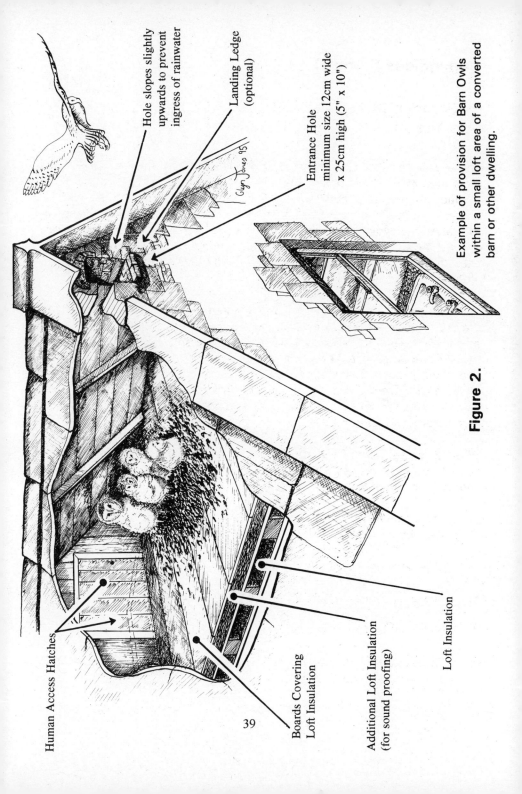

Hole slopes slightly upwards to prevent ingress of rainwater

Landing Ledge (optional)

Entrance Hole minimum size 12cm wide x 25cm high (5" x 10")

Human Access Hatches

Boards Covering Loft Insulation

Additional Loft Insulation (for sound proofing)

Loft Insulation

Example of provision for Barn Owls within a small loft area of a converted barn or other dwelling.

Figure 2.

Glyn Jones 95

39

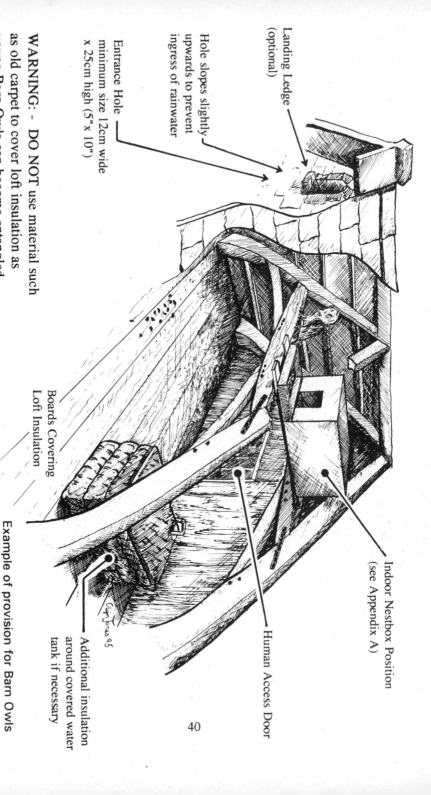

Landing Ledge
(optional)

Hole slopes slightly
upwards to prevent
ingress of rainwater

Entrance Hole
minimum size 12cm wide
x 25cm high (5"x 10")

WARNING: - DO NOT use material such
as old carpet to cover loft insulation as
young Barn Owls can become entangled
in loose thread.

Figure 3.

Boards Covering
Loft Insulation

Example of provision for Barn Owls
within the large loft of a dwelling or
traditional agricultural building.

Additional insulation
around covered water
tank if necessary

Human Access Door

Indoor Nestbox Position
(see Appendix A)

Appendix D.

Example of an Owl entrance hole through a hipped roof.

It is possible to create an owl access hole through the roof itself (see Figure 4). A similar hole can be created during thatching.

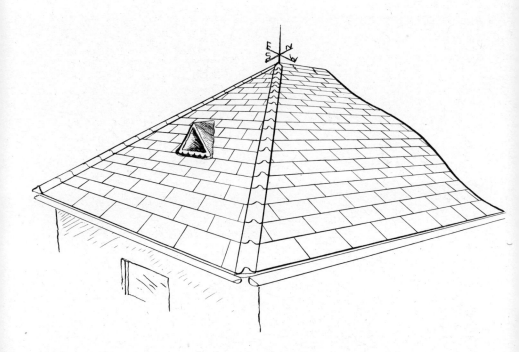

Figure 4.

Appendix E.
Age Determination of Wild Barn Owl Pellets (from dry Locations).

Barn Owl pellets found in dry roosting sites may be compared to the following descriptions:
(See picture No. 6 and note on page 43).

FRESH
Appearance	Black and glossy.
To feel	Wet, quite soft and may blacken fingers slightly.
To break	Pulls apart easily.
Composed of	Wet hair and bone.

SIX DAYS
Appearance	Black and slightly glossy.
To feel	Dry to touch, fairly soft inside.
To break	Pulls apart quite easily.
Composed of	Moist hair and bone.

TEN DAYS
Appearance	Matt black.
To feel	Dry and firm.
To break	Outer surface a bit tough but can be broken by pulling apart.
Composed of	Dry dark grey hair (and bone).

ONE MONTH
Appearance	Very dark grey (matt).
To feel	Dry and quite hard. Crackles when squeezed hard.
To break	Quite tough.
Composed of	Dry dark grey hair (and bone).

EIGHT MONTHS (Very similar to one month).
Appearance	Dark grey (matt).
To feel	Dry and hard. Crackles when squeezed hard.
To break	Quite tough.
Composed of	Dry grey hair (and bone), may contain numerous clothes moth larvae.

FIFTEEN MONTHS

Appearance	Grey with a rough surface.
To feel	Rough and crumbly surface but firm inside, (crackles).
To break	Pulls apart easily.
Composed of	Some grey hair close to surface, interior - grey granules (and bone), may contain clothes moth larvae.

TWENTY ONE MONTHS

Appearance	Grey, rough surface of granules.
To feel	Soft and fragile.
To break	Crumbles easily between fingers.
Composed of	Grey granules and bone, almost powdery. Few if any clothes moth larvae.

THIRTY MONTHS

Appearance	Cluster of bones on layer of grey granules.
To feel	Boney.
To break	Falls apart if not handled carefully.
Composed of	Mostly bone, some coarse grey powder. No larvae.

NOTE: Method and Limitations.

Method

As part of the Barn Conversion Research Project a reference collection of wild Barn Owl pellets was established. When very fresh (wet) Barn owl pellets were found during searches of dry roosting sites (usually farm buildings) they were carefully removed. The samples were then dated and placed in a dry outbuilding alongside other Barn Owl pellet samples. All of the pellets in this collection contained small mammal remains.

Limitations

The drying and decomposition rate of pellets is likely to be variable and may depend on numerous factors e.g. time of year, presence or absence of clothes moths, micro-climate of roosting site and the diet of the birds concerned. However, despite these limitations, pellet age determination holds great potential as a source of information on present and past site occupancy.

The descriptions above can be used <u>as a guide</u> to age determination provided that the pellets in your sample :

a)   Are Barn Owl pellets.

b)   Have laid in a dry position since regurgitation.

c)   Have laid undisturbed and uncovered.

d)   Are not comprised of remains from unusual food items such as birds (identifiable by the presence of feathers) or frogs (identifiable by the absence of hair).

Pellet samples may be posted to the Barn Owl Trust for identification and an estimate of age.

Appendix F.

Useful Contacts.

Barn Owl Trust, Waterleat, Ashburton, Devon, TQ13 7HU. Tel: 01364 653026.

Country Agencies.
Contact your local office for details of a licence holder if a nest inspection is required during the breeding season.

English Nature, Northminster House, Peterborough, PE1 1UA. Tel: 01733 340345.

English Nature Local Area Teams:
Bedfordshire, Cambridgeshire & Northamptonshire. Tel: 01733 391100.
Cumbria. Tel: 01539 45286.
Devon & Cornwall. Tel: 01837 55045 / 01872 86526.
Dorset. Tel: 01929 556688.
East Midlands. Tel: 01476 68431.
Essex, Hertfordshire and London. Tel: 01206 796666/ 0171 831 6922.
Hampshire & Isle of Wight. Tel: 01703 283944.
Humber to Pennines. Tel: 01924 387010.
Kent. Tel: 01233 812525.
North & East Yorkshire. Tel: 01904 432700 / 01969 23447.
Norfolk. Tel: 01603 620558.
Northumbria. Tel: 0191 281 6316/7.
Lancashire, Greater Manchester & Merseyside. Tel: 01942 820342.
Peak District & Derbyshire. Tel: 01629 815095.
Suffolk. Tel: 01284 762218.
Somerset & Avon. Tel: 01823 283211.
Sussex and Surrey. Tel: 01273 476595.
Thames & Chiltern. Tel: 01635 268881.
Hereford, Worcestershire & Gloucestershire. Tel: 01684 560616/7/8.
West Midlands. Tel: 01743 709611.
Wiltshire. Tel: 01380 726344.

Countryside Council for Wales, Plas Penrhos, Ffordd, Penrhos, Bangor, Gwynedd, LL57 2LQ. Tel: 01248 370444.

Countryside Council for Wales Regional Offices:
> North Wales Regional Office. Bangor. Tel: 01248 372333.
> Dyfed/Powys Regional Office. Aberystwyth. Tel: 01970 828551.
> South Wales Regional Office. Cardiff. Tel: 01222 485111.

Scottish Natural Heritage, 12 Hope Terrace, Edinburgh, EH9 2AS. Tel: 0131 447 4784.

Scottish Natural Heritage Regions:
> North West Region. Inverness. Tel: 01463 239431.
> North East Region. Aberdeen. Tel: 01224 642863.
> South West Region, Clydebank. Tel: 0141 951 4488.
> South East Region. Perth. Tel: 01738 444177.

The Wildlife Trusts.

Royal Society for Nature Conservation, The Green, Witham Park Waterside South, Lincoln, LN5 7JR. Tel: 01522 544400.

County Wildlife Trusts:
> Bristol, Bath & Avon. Tel: 01179 268018.
> Bedfordshire, Cambridgeshire, Northamptonshire & Peterborough. Tel: 01223 846363.
> Berks, Bucks & Oxon. Tel: 01865 775476.
> Birmingham & Black Country. Tel: 0121 666 7474.
> Brecknock. Tel: 01874 625708.
> Cheshire. Tel: 01270 610180.
> Cleveland. Tel: 01642 480033.
> Cornwall. Tel: 01872 73939.
> Cumbria. Tel: 015394 32476.
> Derbyshire. Tel: 01332 756610.
> Devon. Tel: 01392 79244.
> Dorset. Tel: 01305 264620.
> Durham. Tel: 01388 488728.
> Dyfed. Tel: 01437 765462.
> Essex. Tel: 01206 729678.
> Glamorgan. Tel: 01656 724100.
> Gloucestershire. Tel: 01452 383333.

County Wildlife Trusts continued:

Guernsey. Tel 014 81 65292.

Gwent. Tel: 01600 715501.

Hampshire & Isle of Wight. Tel: 01703 613636.

Herefordshire. Tel: 01432 356872.

Hertfordshire & Middlesex. Tel: 01727 858901.

Kent. Tel: 01622 662012.

Lancashire. Tel: 01772 324129.

Leicestershire & Rutland. Tel: 01162 553904.

Lincolnshire. Tel: 01507 526667.

London. Tel: 0171 278 6612 / 3.

Manx. Tel: 01624 801985.

Montgomeryshire. Tel: 01938 555654.

Norfolk. Tel: 01603 625540.

Northumberland. Tel: 0191 284 6884.

North Wales. Tel: 01248 351 541.

Nottinghamshire. Tel: 01159 588242.

Radnorshire. Tel: 01597 823298.

Scottish (Edinburgh). Tel: 0131 312 7765.

Shropshire. Tel: 01743 241691.

Sheffield. Tel: 01142 787863.

Somerset. Tel: 01823 451587.

Staffordshire. Tel: 01889 508534.

Suffolk. Tel: 01473 890089.

Surrey. Tel: 01483 488055.

Sussex. Tel: 01273 492630.

Ulster. Tel: 01396 830282.

Warwickshire. Tel: 01203 302912.

Wiltshire. Tel: 01380 725670.

Worcestershire. Tel: 01905 754919.

Yorkshire. Tel: 01904 659570.

APPENDIX G.
Recommendations from the Barn Conversion Research Project Report.

1. The protection afforded to Barn Owls under the Wildlife and Countryside Act 1981 should be extended to include sites which Barn Owls use in the same way that bat roosts and breeding sites are protected.

2. All Local Authority Planning Officers should, as a matter of course, receive sufficient training to enable them to recognise signs of occupation by Barn Owls (droppings, pellets and feathers) and should check for these during site visits.
    Note: This is not a difficult or time consuming task.

3. In the processing of planning applications, Local Authority Planning Officers should inform the relevant Country Agency (English Nature, Countryside Council for Wales or Scottish Natural Heritage) in cases where there is any evidence of possible occupation by Barn Owls.

4. Local Authorities should, without exception, stipulate that provision for Barn Owls is incorporated (into the conversion) at every site where there is any evidence of the current or historic use of the site by Barn Owls.
    Note: The cost of making such provision during a conversion is minimal. Also, experience shows that there are no significant health or nuisance implications.

5. Local Authorities should, as a general policy, stipulate that provision for Barn Owls is incorporated into all barn conversions, irrespective of whether or not Barn Owls are present, unless the site is within an urban area or more than 300 metres above sea level.

6. In cases where planning permission is required for a new agricultural building over three metres high, Local Authorities should stipulate that provision for Barn Owls is incorporated.
    Note: This is inexpensive and can be done in such a way as to prevent the birds having access to the whole interior of the building thereby avoiding possible conflict with salmonella control.